4.99

C000023156

Flute
Grade 1

Pieces
for Trinity College London exams

2017-2020

Published by
Trinity College London Press
www.trinitycollege.com

Registered in England
Company no. 09726123

Printed in England by Caligraving Ltd.

Taking Pictures

Ned Bennett
(b. 1966)

Passepied pour la Jeunesse

from *Ballet de la Jeunesse*

Michel-Richard de Lalande
(1657–1726)

Spooked

Helen Jane Long
(b. 1974)

Cormorant High

Mark Tanner
(b. 1963)

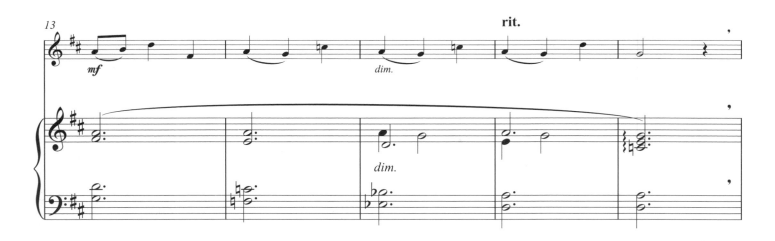

Ronde VI

Tylman Susato
(1500-1561)

Farewell Nancy

Arr. Hywel Davies

Traditional English

Spooked

Helen Jane Long
(b. 1974)

Cormorant High

Mark Tanner
(b. 1963)

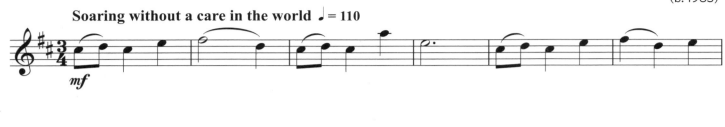

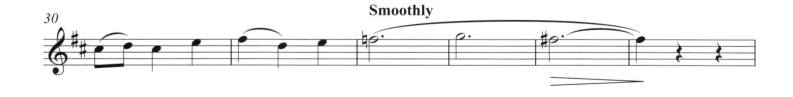

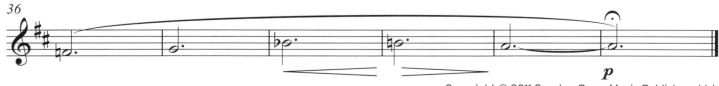

Ronde VI

Tylman Susato
(1500–1561)

Farewell Nancy

Arr. Hywel Davies

Traditional English

Medieval Dance Tune

Arr. Howard Harrison

Anonymous

French Dance

from *The Delightful Pocket Companion for the German Flute* (1763)

Anonymous
18th Century

One More for the Road

Helen Madden
(b. 1974)